Sad, Mad, or Glad

By Liza Charlesworth

ISBN: 978-1-339-02678-7

Art Director: Tannaz Fassihi; Designer: Tanya Chernyak
Photos © Getty Images.

3 4 5 6 7 8 9 10   68   32 31 30 29 28 27 26 25 24

Printed in Jiaxing, China. First printing, August 2023.

SCHOLASTIC

Drop! This kid's snack
fell on the grass.
He is so sad.

The sun is so hot.
But this kid is glad.
She can get wet!

This tot did not get a nap.
So he is sad and mad.
He is a grump!

This gal is so glad
to be on a sled.
She can go, go, go!

Can this kid go to class? No!
He must rest in his bed.
He is sad to be sick.

The twins got a pet.
It is a big black dog.
"We are so glad!" they yell.

It is OK not to be glad.
But if you are sad or mad,
a hug can help a lot!